First, let's find out a few things about you!

My name is Princess _____

I am _____ years old.   I am in the _____ grade.

Kingdom (city / state): _____

My favorite princess is: _____

She is my favorite princess because: _____

_____

If I could have a castle anywhere in the world, it would be in:

_____

What would your dream ball gown look like?

_____

_____

Are you like BELLE?

In her small village, Belle dreamed of love and adventure in faraway places. One day, she hoped to have the same exciting adventures as the characters in her favorite books.

Her wishes came true beyond her wildest dreams after she arrived at an enchanted castle and met a brooding beast.

Tender-hearted and fearless, Belle saw past the Beast's rough exterior and broke a spell that turned her new friend from a beast into a handsome prince.

This princess always looks for the beauty within others.

Which Princess Are You?

Published by
Louis Weber, C.E.O.,
Publications International, Ltd.
7373 North Cicero Avenue, Lincolnwood, Illinois 60712

Ground Floor, 59 Gloucester Place, London W1U 8JJ

Customer Service: 1-800-595-8484
or customer_service@pilbooks.com

www.pilbooks.com

p i kids is a trademark of Publications International, Ltd., and is registered in the United States.

8 7 6 5 4 3 2 1

ISBN-13: 978-1-4508-2509-2
ISBN-10: 1-4508-2509-5

Let's find your princess personality!

First, read all about what makes each princess special,
then find the qualities you share with each one.

Next, take these fun and quick quizzes to find out which Disney Princess is just
like you! Answer the questions, then turn to the answer key in the back.

✓ **Check the qualities that you admire most in Belle.**

📘 honest   📘 stubborn

📘 loves to read   📘 mature

📘 polite   📘 sarcastic

📘 adventurous   📘 courageous

📘 dreamer   📘 hero

In which way are you most like Belle?

_____

_____

_____

_____

_____

Are you like CINDERELLA?

Cinderella awoke each morning with the hope that one day, her dreams of finding love and happiness would come true.

Forced to serve her stepmother and stepsisters as a servant in her own home, Cinderella fulfilled her duties with gentle grace, dreaming each day that she would find someone to treat her with kindness.

With help from her friends and the Fairy Godmother, Cinderella was able to attend a royal ball. There she found her faithful prince, who helped make all of her dreams come true.

Cinderella always believes in love!

✔ **Check the qualities that you admire most in Cinderella.**

- charming
- gentle
- daydreamer
- kindhearted
- selfless

- kind
- grateful
- hopeful
- faithful
- gracious

In which way are you most like Cinderella?

_____

_____

_____

_____

_____

Are you like ARIEL?

Ariel was a headstrong young mermaid who was fascinated by the human world. Every day she longed to learn more about life above the surface of the ocean, and daydreamed about what it would be like to live on land.

When she saved Prince Eric from a sinking ship, Ariel fell in love with him, and decided to strike a risky deal with the sea witch to become human. With the help of her friends, Ariel made her dreams of living on land and marrying Prince Eric come true.

Ariel is a determined princess who sticks to her dreams, and never gives up.

✓ **Check the qualities that you admire most in Ariel.**

independent

determined

clever

curious

adventurous

daring

open-minded

defiant

risk-taker

hopeful

In which way are you most like Ariel?

_____

_____

_____

_____

_____

Are you like POCAHONTAS?

Pocahontas was a spirited Native American who loved to run with the wind and spend time with her friends in the forest.

When a boat from a faraway place arrived on the shores of her tribe's land, Pocahontas met John Smith, the captain. Despite warnings from her tribe that their visitors were dangerous, Pocahontas and John Smith became friends.

When Pocahontas's tribe and John Smith's crew began to fight, the two friends showed both groups that through friendship and understanding, they could overcome their differences.

Pocahontas is a brave and wise princess.

Check the qualities that you admire most in Pocahontas.

proud   strong

wise   independent

free-spirited   athletic

noble   mischievous

brave   leader

In which way are you most like Pocahontas?

_____

_____

_____

_____

_____

Are you like SLEEPING BEAUTY?

Sleeping Beauty grew up in a cottage hidden in the woods. There, three good fairies raised her in secret to keep her safe from an evil fairy's spell until her sixteenth birthday.

On that day, Sleeping Beauty was walking in the woods when she met the man of her dreams and fell in love. When she arrived home, the fairies whisked her away to the castle where she would be crowned a princess.

In the castle, the evil fairy appeared and put the princess under a spell. Soon after, her true love came to the rescue, and broke the spell with a kiss.

Sleeping Beauty knows that dreams can come true!

✔ Check the qualities that you admire most in Sleeping Beauty.

♡ kind   ♡ graceful

♡ selfless   ♡ simple

♡ obedient   ♡ responsible

♡ loving   ♡ loyal

♡ thoughtful   ♡ romantic

In which way are you most like Sleeping Beauty?

_____

_____

_____

_____

_____

Are you like Snow White?

Snow White was a beautiful young princess under the rule of a vain queen. When a prince fell in love with her, the jealous queen feared that Snow White's beauty had become greater than her own, and she sent Snow White away. Cast off into the woods, Snow White found friends in the forest animals. They led her to the cottage of the Seven Dwarfs, where Snow White was invited to stay.

Each day Snow White wished that her prince would find her again. When the jealous queen put Snow White under a spell, her prince arrived to save her.

Kindness and patience are Snow White's greatest virtues!

✓ **Check the qualities that you admire most in Snow White.**

🍎 gentle   🍎 nurturing

🍎 sweet   🍎 polite

🍎 cheerful   🍎 faithful

🍎 optimistic   🍎 trusting

🍎 charming   🍎 musical

In which way are you most like Snow White?

_____

_____

_____

_____

_____

Are you like TIANA?

When Tiana's dreams of owning a restaurant were suddenly dashed, she wished on a star for help. Instead of help, a frog appeared, and asked Tiana to kiss him. If she agreed, he would return to his human form, Prince Naveen, and make her dreams come true.

Tiana kissed Naveen, and they both became frogs! The two traveled deep into the bayou to ask Mama Odie for help. Mama Odie taught Tiana and Naveen that they must find what they need in order to get what they want...and when they both found love, all of their dreams came true.

Tiana knows what she needs!

Check the qualities that you admire most in Tiana.

♡ hard-working   ♡ responsible

♡ ambitious   ♡ disciplined

♡ wishful   ♡ zestful

♡ brave   ♡ stubborn

♡ resourceful   ♡ independent

In which way are you most like Tiana?

_____

_____

_____

_____

_____

Are you like RAPUNZEL?

Rapunzel wished to find the source of the mysterious lights that appeared in the sky each year on her birthday. However, Mother Gothel forbade her to leave the tower, and made Rapunzel believe that the outside world was dangerous and scary.

One day, Rapunzel convinced Flynn Rider to escort her out of the tower and into town.

On her journey, Rapunzel learned that the lights were lanterns, launched each year to find a missing princess — her!

Rapunzel overcomes her fears, and finds much more than she had ever dreamed of!

✓ **Check the qualities that you admire most in Rapunzel.**

kind   bright

feisty   spirited

hopeful   cheerful

friendly   sheltered

strong   open-minded

In which way are you most like Rapunzel?

_____

_____

_____

_____

_____

Are you like
JASMINE?

Princess Jasmine lived all of her life guarded behind palace walls. She longed to experience the wonder and adventure that the outside world promised.

One day, Jasmine decided to leave the palace. Disguised as a peasant, Jasmine explored the market and met a young man, Aladdin, who took her on an adventure that she would never forget. Zooming across the sky on his magic carpet, Jasmine saw the world, and found the life she had wished for.

Jasmine believes that you must go out and find your dreams!

✓ **Check the qualities that you admire most in Jasmine.**

headstrong

clever

free-spirited

curious

resourceful

adventurous

honest

open-minded

confident

caring

In which way are you most like Jasmine?

_____

_____

_____

_____

_____

Are you like MULAN?

Mulan wanted to bring honor to her family, but despite her best efforts, she only brought them grief.

When Mulan's aging father was drafted into the army for another term, Mulan decided to take his place and complete his service. Mulan disguised herself as a young man, and reported to her father's training camp.

Mulan overcame many of her fears and grew to be a strong and resilient soldier. In a fierce battle, brave Mulan helped rescue her country from invaders, and brought honor to her family and her entire country.

Mulan's hard work gave her more than she could ever wish for!

✔ Check the qualities that you admire most in Mulan.

- independent
- courageous
- mischievous
- athletic
- brave

- honorable
- secretive
- self-reliant
- determined
- heroic

In which way are you most like Mulan?

_____

_____

_____

_____

_____

My Friends

A princess's friends say a lot about her personality!

My friends are:
- A shy
- B adventurous

Our favorite place to go is:
- A the park
- B the pool

When we get together, we like to:
- A sing and dance
- B collect things

Our favorite games to play are:
- A board games
- B outdoor games

Our favorite movies are about:
- A love stories
- B adventure

Turn to page 44

Wishes & Dreams

Which princess's wishes and dreams are just like yours?

In your dreams:
- A true love finds you
- B you find true love

You like to wish on:
- A the future
- B the stars

Which one of these things would you wish for?
- A a beautiful dress
- B a place of your own

When you wish for something:
- A you wait for your wish to come true
- B you help make it come true

For your dreams to come true, you must:
- A believe that they will come true
- B work hard

Turn to page 44

Family

Which family would suit a princess like you?

For fun, you and your family like to:
- A play games outside
- B create new things

Which activity would your family prefer:
- A camping
- B going to a museum

Your family would describe you as:
- A spirited
- B loyal

Your family's values are:
- A traditional
- B new-age

Your parents are:
- A strict
- B open-minded

Turn to page 44

Music

Which princess shares your musical taste?

Which of these instruments would you like to play?

- A guitar
- B harp

You like to listen to music that is:

- A loud
- B quiet

You like to dance to:

- A fast songs
- B slow songs

Your favorite songs are:

- A silly songs
- B love songs

When you hear a song you like:

- A you listen to it over and over
- B you listen to it a few times

Turn to page 44

Fashion

Which princess shares your signature style?

When you go shopping:

A you search for trendy fashions

B you don't have a clue what you're looking for

On the first day of school you wear:

A your newest outfit

B something from last year

People would describe your look as:

A trendy

B sporty

You like clothes that are:

A fashionable

B comfortable

At the end of the day, your clothes:

A say something about your personality

B are just clothes, no big deal

Turn to page 45

Food

Find out which princess has the same taste buds as you!

What would you rather put on top of your pizza?

- A veggies
- B sausage

Your favorite meals:

- A are usually eaten at home
- B are cooked in a restaurant

One of your favorite treats is:

- A fruit
- B doughnuts

When you're hungry, you want:

- A something sweet
- B something savory

Which one of these foods would you rather cook?

- A cookies
- B spicy soup

Turn to page 45

Crown

What kind of crown would suit a princess like you?

You would like to wear your crown:

- A every once in a while
- B all the time

Your crown would be a symbol of:

- A a wonderful family
- B true love

Your crown would be:

- A gold
- B coral

Your crown will be decorated with:

- A jewels
- B seashells

You would share your crown with:

- A your best friend
- B your hero

Turn to page 45

Hobbies

Which princess has similar hobbies as you?

When you're bored, you usually:
- A work on a project you've already started
- B find something new to work on or create

The books you read are all about:
- A how to do / make things
- B adventure

Which activity would you choose?
- A paint a picture
- B read a book

Your favorite subject in school is:
- A science
- B history

On a Saturday afternoon, you'd like to:
- A explore the outdoors
- B go for a walk with a friend

Turn to page 45

Goals

Every princess has a goal!

When you set a goal for yourself:
- A you believe 100% that you will achieve your goal
- B you try your best and hope to achieve your goal

The goals you set are usually:
- A in school (tests, grades)
- B in activities (sports, competitions)

Who knows about your goals?
- A everyone
- B a few people

Who has helped you achieve your goals?
- A your family
- B your friends

Your friends think your goals are:
- A ambitious
- B heroic

Turn to page 46

Manners

Match up your manners!

If someone is rude to your friends:

💗 A   you make sure that your friends are okay

💗 B   you ask the person to apologize to your friends

When all of your friends are together:

💗 A   you do everything to make sure the group is happy

💗 B   you sit back and let the fun create itself

When someone does something nice for you:

💗 A   you say thank you

💗 B   you do something nice for them

To thank a friend, you:

💗 A   write a thank you note

💗 B   call them to say thank you

Your friends would describe you as:

💗 A   passive

💗 B   spirited

Turn to page 46

Pets

What kind of a princess pet do you prefer?

Which pet would you prefer?
A cat
B frog

You would like to have a pet that is:
A big and snuggly
B easy to carry around

Pets should be:
A reliable
B full of surprises

Your perfect pet:
A likes to sleep on a pillow
B likes to sleep in the grass

Your ideal pet:
A likes all of your friends
B is a little shy at first

Turn to page 46

Travel

Which princess would be your travel buddy?

What's the most interesting thing about faraway places?

- A the people
- B everything

Whom would you take with you on your journey?

- A anyone who wants to go
- B a few close friends

When you think about where you'd like to travel:

- A you think of one, specific place
- B you can name several places

Which of these places would you like to visit?

- A Europe
- B Africa

How do you like to travel?

- A by boat
- B by plane

Turn to page 46

Dream House

Which princess would like to visit your dream house?

Your dream house is:
- A on top of a beautiful hill
- B deep in the forest

The flowers in your yard are:
- A daisies
- B roses

Your dream house is painted:
- A white
- B yellow

You live:
- A close to town
- B out in the country

Your favorite room in the house is:
- A the ballroom
- B the library

Turn to page 47

Dream Car

Find your princess ride.

Your dream car is:
- A cute
- B sporty

You like to ride your bike:
- A slow
- B fast

What color would your dream car be?
- A red
- B blue

What would your carriage look like?
- A simple and elegant
- B royal and regal

Which is cooler?
- A big car
- B small car

Turn to page 47

Dream Prince

Find out who your dream prince is.

Your favorite thing to do together is:
- A   sing
- B   dance

Your dream prince is:
- A   your hero
- B   your best friend

One of his hobbies is:
- A   horseback riding
- B   reading

Your dream prince is:
- A   a sportsman
- B   a gentleman

He knows that you like:
- A   diamonds
- B   pearls

Turn to page 47

Games & Sports

Which princess would you want on your team?

You would rather play:
- A defense
- B offense

You prefer to:
- A play on a team
- B play by yourself

At the end of the game:
- A you'll do anything to win
- B win or lose, it doesn't matter

Which of these sports do you like?
- A tennis
- B baseball

Do you keep score?
- A yes
- B no

Turn to page 47

Hairstyle

Which princess would like your hairstyle the most?

How do you like to style your hair?
- A you like to try different styles all the time
- B your hair is the same style every day

The length of your hair is:
- A long
- B short

Doing your hair in the morning:
- A takes a long time
- B takes no time at all

When you go out, your hair is:
- A up
- B down

Your favorite hair accessories are:
- A ribbons
- B headbands

Turn to page 48

Dancing

Which princess are you like on the dance floor?

Your favorite thing to wear when you dance is:
- A something that sparkles
- B a beautiful dress

Your favorite music is:
- A loud and exciting
- B quiet and soothing

You prefer to dance:
- A with your friends
- B with a partner

Which of these dances do you like more?
- A jazz
- B waltz

You like dancing to music that is:
- A fast
- B slow

Turn to page 48

Accessories

What your accessories say about you.

Your favorite earrings are:
- A   as big as they can be
- B   simple and sweet

Which one would you choose?
- A   jeweled necklace
- B   beaded necklace

Your favorite outfit would look best with:
- A   ballet flats
- B   heels

You're more comfortable in:
- A   pants
- B   skirts

Bracelets should be:
- A   big and flashy
- B   elegant

Turn to page 48

Dream Job

Which princess shares your aspirations?

One of your favorite hobbies is:
- A sharing food with your friends
- B reading a great book

You like to spend time:
- A with lots of friends
- B in quiet rooms

With your friends, you like to:
- A help lead activities
- B help teach them new things

Your dream job:
- A is your ultimate goal
- B is fun to think about

Work should be:
- A challenging
- B rewarding

Turn to page 48

Answers

My Friends (page 24)

You answered mostly As:
Your friends are just like Sleeping Beauty's! They prefer a low-key place to hang out. With these friends around, you can have a good time anywhere!

You answered mostly Bs:
Your friends are just like Ariel's! They like to get out and explore everything they can. This group of pals is sure to lead to some exciting times!

Wishes & Dreams (page 25)

You answered mostly As:
Your wishes and dreams are more like Snow White's. Patient and kind, you know that if you keep believing in your dreams, everything you've wished for will come true.

You answered mostly Bs:
Your wishes and dreams are more like Tiana's. Resilient and resourceful, you want to do everything you can to make sure your dreams come true!

Family (page 26)

You answered mostly As:
Your family is like Pocahontas's! Tradition and respect lie at the core of your family, and you all enjoy learning from each other and with each other.

You answered mostly Bs:
Your family is like Belle's! Free-spirited and unconventional, your family likes to rock the boat!

Music (page 27)

You answered mostly As:
You and Rapunzel like the same kind of music! Silly and sweet, you could rock the crowd at the Snuggly Duckling together!

You answered mostly Bs:
You and Cinderella have the same taste in quiet, simple love songs. You'd rather be on the dance floor waltzing away than jamming out in a crowd.

Answers

Fashion (page 28)

You answered mostly As:
You and Jasmine have the same sense of fashion. Your clothes must be hip, trendy, and say something about who you are.

You answered mostly Bs:
You and Mulan have the same thoughts when it comes to fashion! As long as it's comfortable and fun, you're happy.

Food (page 29)

You answered mostly As:
You and Rapunzel like the same kinds of food! You know what your favorites are, and you stick with them.

You answered mostly Bs:
You and Tiana both like delightful and delicious food. You'd be a good candidate to help Tiana spice up her new restaurant!

Crown (page 30)

You answered mostly As:
You and Rapunzel would wear the same kind of crown. Simple and elegant, this crown would grace your head only for fancy occasions.

You answered mostly Bs:
You and Ariel would wear your crown of sea treasures every day! You love being a princess, and you want everyone to know it.

Hobbies (page 31)

You answered mostly As:
You and Rapunzel like the same hobbies! You have a passion for everything that you do, and you'll spend a lot of time making sure that each one of your projects is perfect.

You answered mostly Bs:
You and Belle like the same hobbies! You have an open mind and love to broaden your horizons by trying out new, fun things.

Answers

Goals (page 32)

You answered mostly As:
You and Tiana look at goals the same way. Pick one, stick with it, work hard, and do everything you can to achieve it.

You answered mostly Bs:
You and Mulan prefer to make lots of small goals that eventually lead to one, big goal. Mulan achieved many goals, but the most important was bringing honor to her family.

Manners (page 33)

You answered mostly As:
You and Cinderella have the same excellent manners, and believe that being polite will bring good things back to you.

You answered mostly Bs:
You and Belle have the same good manners, and believe that the people around you should, too! If they don't, you and Belle will be sure to let them know about it.

Pets (page 34)

You answered mostly As:
You and Jasmine prefer big, cuddly, loyal pets like Rajah! Snuggly and fierce, Rajah will always watch your back.

You answered mostly Bs:
You and Rapunzel like to have slick little pals like Pascal, who are always there for you in a pinch.

Travel (page 35)

You answered mostly As:
You and Ariel would be excellent traveling buddies! You want to visit places that are a little familiar, but still have lots of interesting things to see.

You answered mostly Bs:
You and Jasmine could travel the world together! You both want to visit exotic places and learn everything you can about each place.

Answers

Dream House (page 36)

You answered mostly As:
Cinderella would love to visit your dream house! You two would have a fabulous time lounging in your beautiful home.

You answered mostly Bs:
Belle can't wait to come over to your dream house. You both have similar tastes and have the same laid-back lifestyle.

Dream Car (page 37)

You answered mostly As:
You and Ariel would like the same kind of dream car: cute and comfortable. You would like to take all of your friends on a cruise through town.

You answered mostly Bs:
Your dream car is very similar to Aladdin's magic carpet! Both you and Jasmine would like to zip around town in something sassy!

Dream Prince (page 38)

You answered mostly As:
Prince Phillip is your favorite! You and Sleeping Beauty both get swept away by grand, heroic gestures.

You answered mostly Bs:
Your dream prince is the Beast! You and Belle both like princes that sweep you off of your feet with kindness.

Games & Sports (page 39)

You answered mostly As:
You and Tiana would be excellent teammates. You work hard and are determined to win.

You answered mostly Bs:
You and Belle view games and sports the same way: they're fun, but not that big of a deal.

Answers

Hairstyle (page 40)

You answered mostly As:
You would look great with Rapunzel's hair!
Light and long, you'll be a hit with
anyone you meet.

You answered mostly Bs:
You would look amazing with
Snow White's hair! Dark and sleek,
you'll be the belle of the ball
every time.

Dancing (page 41)

You answered mostly As:
You and Tiana would have a blast on the
dance floor! Footloose and fancy-free,
you could dance to the band all night!

You answered mostly Bs:
You and Sleeping Beauty both like to
dance slowly, with grace and elegance.
The princes will be lining up to
dance with you!

Accessories (page 42)

You answered mostly As:
You and Jasmine like accessories that
make a statement. If you're going to
put on jewelry, it better stand out!

You answered mostly Bs:
Cinderella would like to have a look in
your jewelry box! You both like accessories
that are simple, and quietly accent
your already beautiful appearance.

Dream Job (page 43)

You answered mostly As:
You like a challenge, so you'd prefer to be
the boss, just like Tiana! You'd like to start
your own business and lead it by example.

You answered mostly Bs:
Becoming a teacher or a librarian would
be an excellent job for you! Just like Belle,
you enjoy helping people learn
about new things.